CONTENTS

CUT-OUTS. Some of the games in this Annual ask you to cut out pictures. If you don't want to do this, trace the picture you have been asked to cut out onto another piece of paper and colour it in. You'll have just as much fun using this to play the game!

SESAME STREET ANNUAL 1993, published by MARVEL COMICS LTD, 13/15 Arundel Street, London WC2R 3DX, is produced in cooperation with the Children's Television Workshop (CTW).©1992 CTW. Sesame Street MUPPETS © Jim Henson Productions, Inc. 1992. All rights reserved. All contents are owned by CTW and may not be reprinted without their permission. Sesame Street and the Sesame Street sign are registered trademarks and Service Marks of CTW. Printed in Italy.

THIS BOOK BELONGS TO:

Steven
John
Kiynn

SPLISH SPLASH

Sounds in the Bath

SKYWRITING

On some spring days, the sky is filled with fluffy white clouds. Sometimes the clouds look like animals and other things. Can you see clouds that look like a fat cat? Which cloud looks like a flat hat?

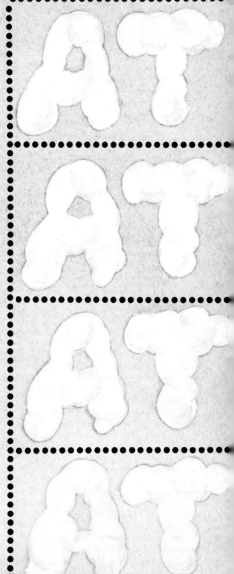

Cut out these letter clouds to make word clouds. Put them in the sky next to the other letter clouds. What words did you make?

illustration © Carol Inouye

PASTA PALS

What could be better than sharing a favourite food with a favourite friend? Snuffy's favourite food is spaghetti, and his favourite friend is Big Bird.
You can help them enjoy their dinner by following the maze through the noodles.
Start at Snuffy or Big Bird's fork. Then follow the path with your finger and then your crayon to see where the maze ends.

What is your favourite food? Who is your best friend? What do you like to share with your best friend?

CRAYON

HOCKERMAN

illustration by Dennis Hockerman

WHEN I HEAR A SONG

When I hear a song that is booming and loud,
I think of an elephant caught in a crowd,
Of lions and tigers and noisy baboons
Who are banging on drums and popping balloons.

When I hear a song that is terribly fast,
I think of a rocket that's flying right past,
A bright silver aeroplane high up in the sky
While a bird dips and dances as the plane passes by.

hen I hear a song that is dreamy and slow,
hink of a flower that's starting to grow
the woods, near a lake, where a spider and ant
e taking a walk on the leaf of a plant.

hen you hear a song that is happy and gay,
you think of an elf on a bright, sunny day?
your feet feel like dancing? Do you wish you could fly?
you think you would like to jump up in the sky?

Can you sing
a song that is
booming and
loud? Can
you sing a
song that is
terribly fast?

poem by Dina Anastasio
illustration © Nancy Cunningham

D IS FOR DOG

It's a dog's day in the park. What would you do if *you* were a dog? Can you find another animal in the picture whose name begins with the letter D?

EVERGREEN

FOREST

The letters E and F are hiding in this evergreen forest. Can you find them? What things do you see whose names begin with the letter E or F?

Illustration by Melinda Fabian

15

Now, where on earth . . .?

Ernie wants to go out and play in the rain.

But where are his raincoat , his umbrella , and his boots ?

Can you help Ernie find his rain things?

Look all over this page.

Put circles around Ernie's rain things.

WHAT IF?

What would happen if you talked to a monke and it talked back? What would you say? What would you do?

What would happen if everybody could fly? What would you say? What would you do?

18

What would happen if you found a hidden treasure?
What would you say?
What would you do?

What would happen if you were a daddy?
What would you say?
What would you do?

tions by Marsha Winborn

CASTLE IN

You can visit a make-believe castle in the clouds. Just fold the pages so that the red dots meet, like this:

Can you find all the things that are shaped like a circle?

G. MARTI

THE SKY

SHADES OF COLOUR

There are eight different coloured groups of crayons on this page, but there's a crayon missing from the middle of each pile. Write in the correct colour in the space from the list below. Then, colour in the spaces with your own crayons, matching up the colours!

GREEN BLUE ORANGE PURPLE RED YELLOW GREY BROWN

Illustration © Paul Riche

OPPOSITES ARE

Big Bird is big. He isn't small.
Little Bird is short, not tall.
Small is not like tall at all.
Big and small are opposites.

Who's big? Who's little?

big

small

Elmo's thoughtful. He isn't rude.
Oscar's in a grouchy mood.
Each has a different attitude.
Thoughtful and rude are opposites.

How is a thoughtful person different from a rude person?

rude

thoughtful

24

NOT ALIKE

...nie's messy. He isn't neat.
...ert says, "Ernie, wipe your feet!"
...eing neat's no easy feat.
...essy and neat are opposites.

messy

neat

What is a messy person like?
What is a neat person like?

...uffy's quiet. He isn't loud.
...airie shouts 'cause she's so proud.
...uffy's shy in any crowd.
...ese two friends are opposites.

...y are Prairie
...n and Snuffy
...erent from each
...er? When do you
...as shy as Snuffy?
...t makes you as
...d as Prairie Dawn?

shy

proud

25

rover and the Beanstalk

Overnight a magic beanstalk grew up, up, up into the sky.

Brave Grover wants to get to the pot of gold at the top.

Use your finger to follow the path from Grover to the pot of gold.

Then use your pencil.

Now follow the path to the beans.

Help Grover find the flowers.

27

Start an Indoor Garden...

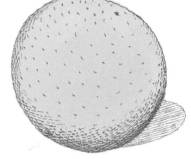

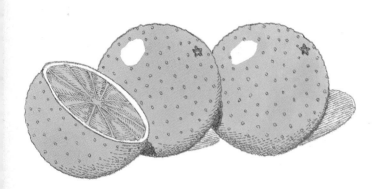

This is what you'll need:
a pair of scissors
an empty milk container
6 orange or grapefruit seeds
a few handfuls of soil
some water

This is what you do:

① Ask an adult to cut the milk container in half, like this:

Fill it about 2 inches deep with soil. Save the rest of the soil.

② Put the 6 seeds on top of the soil. Cover the seeds with about a ½ inch of soil.

③ Moisten the soil and put the container in a dark place for two weeks.

④ When the seeds begin to sprout, put the container in a sunny window. In a few weeks, you will have a small green plant.

illustration © Rodica Prato

QUARTET OF GROUCH SNACKS

A **qu**artet is four of something. Here is a **qu**artet of **qu**ick grouch snacks. Without **qu**estion, they are **qu**ite yucky — just the way we like them. They are perfect recipes for Grungetta the Grouch **Qu**een and me!

The letters Q and U are hidden in the picture. Circle each one you find. How many of each are there?

Illustration by Maggie Swanson

A FEAST

PIN THE MUSHROOM ON THE PIZZA

You can play this game by yourself or with some friends.

1. Draw a pizza on a big piece of paper and hang it on the wall.
2. Cut out the mushrooms on this page.
3. Take turns closing your eyes and trying to tape a mushroom on the pizza.

POTATO GAME

Play this game with a group of friends.

1. Pick something that will be the "Potato," such as a rolled-up sock.
2. Decide who will be the Leader. The rest of the players stand in a circle around the Leader.
3. The players pass around the Potato.
4. The Leader tries to tag whoever is holding the Potato. The player who is tagged while holding the Potato becomes the next Leader.

Illustrations by Fred Schrier

OF GAMES

T BOILED BEANS AND BACON

**ay this game with one or more
ends.**

One player who is "It" goes out of the room.
The other players hide an object, such as a
ck. When the object is hidden, they call out
t boiled beans and bacon, it's hidden and
be taken!"

he player who is "It" comes back to look
the object. When he or she gets near the
ct, call out "Hot." When the player is far,
out "Cold." When he or she is very close
ery far, call out "Very hot" or "Very cold."
When the object is found, choose another
er to
It."

PAT-A-CAKE

**You can clap to the beat by yourself
or with a friend.**

Pat-a-cake, pat-a-cake, baker's man,
Bake me a cake as fast as you can.
Roll it and pat it and mark it with "B,"
And put it in the oven for Baby and me.

Photo by Caroline Monaghan Pallat

In My Room

by *Dina Anastasio*

Last night I put two shoes away;
Now one of them is gone.
I'd like to find my missing shoe
So I can put both on.

It isn't on the table
With my paintbrush and my clay.
It isn't in the corner
Where I read the other day.

It isn't near the window
Where I saw a butterfly,
Or underneath my picture
Of a rainbow in the sky.

Wait!—It's there, beside the tail
That's wagging by my chair.
My faithful doggy, Rover,
Must have put it there.

Can you say "hello" in all
these different languages?

Cooee
(koo-EE)
Aboriginal

Konnichiwa
(ko-NEE-chee-WAH)
Japanese

Wei
(way)
Chinese

Háo
(how)
Sioux (American Indian)

Bonjour
(bon-ZHOOR)
French

Jambo
(JAHM-bo)
Swahili

Hola
(OH-la)
Spanish

Privet
(preev-YET)
Russian

Portuguese

PLANET, SWEET PLANET

Namaste
(nam-AHS-tee)

Shalom
(shah-LOME)
Hebrew

Aloha
(ah-LO-ha)
Hawaiian

M'bolo
(mm-BO-lo)
Bulu (Cameroon)

Hello
(hel-LO)
English

Sabaidi
(sub-EYE-dee)
Laotian

Güten Tag
(GU-ten TAHG)
German

Salaam
(sah-LAHM)
Arabic

MY WORLD

This is our home;
    it's a small window box.
It's a world Ernie built
    using thimbles and blocks,
Where we slide on a spoon
    and we swing on a thread,
Where the bees and
    the butterflies fly overhead.

This is my room;
    it's the best place to be.
It's a world of its own —
    it's a world just for me,
Where I'll daydream today
    and I'll night-dream tonig[ht,]
Where my pigeons and I
    sip on cups of moonlight[.]

his is my street;
  it's a place you all know.
's a world full of neighbours
  who all say hello,
here a Grouch in a bin
  is a monster's best friend,
here a big fluffy bird
  likes to play and pretend.

This is the Earth;
  it's a place that we love.
It's a beautiful world
  with a blue sky above,
Where a crystal clear lake
  sits near mountains so tall,
Where the sun sends a warm,
  beaming kiss to us all.

Poem by Sheila Sweeny
Illustrations by Ellen Appleby

THE MEAL

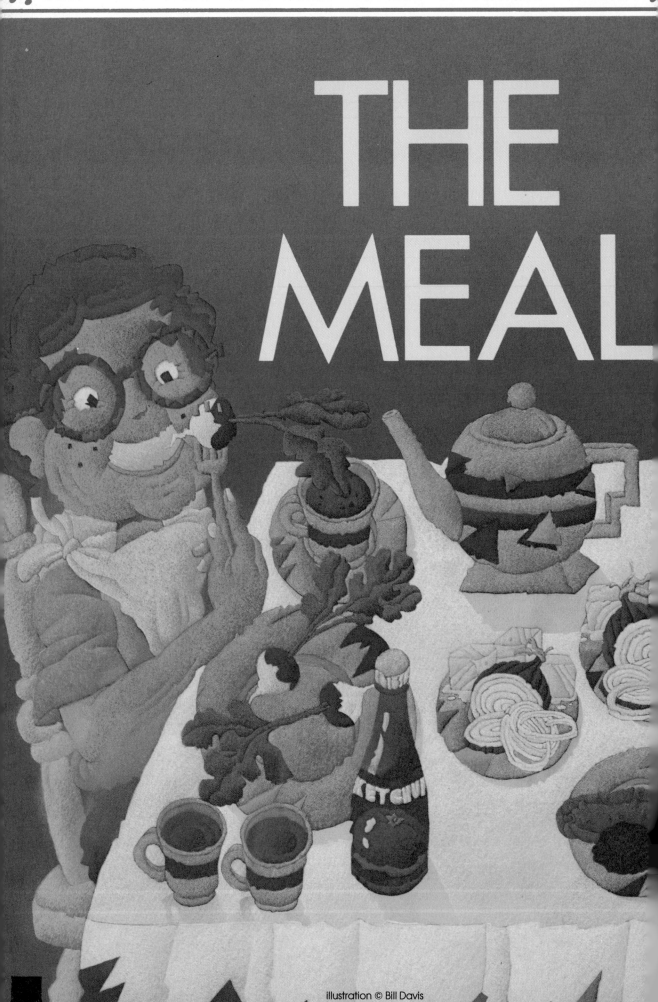

illustration © Bill Davis

Timothy Tompkins had turnips and tea.
The turnips were tiny.
He ate at least three.
And then, for dessert,
He had onions and ice.
He liked that so much
That he ordered it twice.
He had two cups of ketchup,
A prune and some honey.
"Delicious," said Timothy.
"Well worth the money!"
He folded his napkin
And hastened to add,
"It's one of the loveliest breakfasts I've had."

From DOGS AND DRAGONS, TREES & DREAMS by Karla Kuskin. Copyright © 1980 by Karla Kuskin.
Reprinted by permission of Harper and Row, Publishers, Inc.

Now draw your favourite breakfast on the table.

SHIP TO SHORE

Imagine what it would be like to go up, up, up until you reached the stars. What would it be like to swim in the ocean - down, down, down - until you were able to touch the bottom of the sea? Which way is up? Which way is down? Use your finger and then your crayon to find your way from START to FINISH in each path.

FINISH

FINISH

Illustrations by Patrick Girouard

Whoever heard of a purple pig?
by Grover

Start at the purple man.

Today I met a **purple** man
Who wore a **purple** wig.
He smiled and said, "I'm **Purple** Dan.
I saw a **purple** pig."

"You saw a . . . **purple** . . . pig?!?" I said.
"Where is the piggy now?"
"Beats me." Dan shook his **purple** head.
"Go ask the **purple** cow."

Go to the purple cow.

"Oh **purple** cow, do you know where
The **purple** piggy went?"
"I think," said Cow, "It's over there,
Inside the **purple** tent."

Go to the purple tent.

I found the tent and went inside
And saw a **purple** duck.
"Where does the **purple** piggy hide?"
She said, "Quack . . . **purple** truck."

Go to the purple truck.

Now flying 'round the **purple** truck
I saw a **purple** bee.
He buzzed, "Hello, my name izzz Chuck.
You're s'pozzzzed to follow me."

Follow the purple bee.

I followed Chuck past **purple** trees,
And past a **purple** chair.
I cried, "Where is the piggy, *please?*"
"I know!" said **Purple** Bear.

Go to the purple bear.

"The **purple** pig lives in a house
That's by a **purple** brook."
So, creeping quiet as a mouse,
I went to have a look.

Go to the purple house.

I snuck up to the **purple** door
All made of **purple** straw.
I gave 1 knock . . . 2 . . . 3 . . . then 4–
Now what do you think I saw?

What's inside the house?

illustration © Larry Difiori

IF I HAD A RUBBER DUCKIE

by_____

write a word on each blank line

If I had a rubber duckie all my own, I would name

it_____. We would swim

together and take_____together.

My rubber duckie would be my favourite colour, which

is_____. That's the same colour

as my_____.

illustration © Ajin

If I had a rubber duckie, I would share it with my friend

_____. Of course, I would also let

_____ play with it. (Sometimes.)

My rubber duckie would like every room in my house,

but its favourite room would be the_____.

It would like all of my books, but the book it would like best

is_____. Maybe we'll read it tonight.

And if my rubber duckie could sing, its favourite song

would be_____. That's my

favourite song too.

Quacking Up

In each group, which duck is not like the others?
Tell how it is different.

illustration © Ann Wilson

ERNIE'S CAT PYJAMAS

It was time for bed. Ernie put on his new pyjamas, the ones with the little cat pictures. He said good night to Bert and snuggled under the covers.

As he began to fall asleep, Ernie thought he saw something move on his pyjamas. Suddenly, a fluffy, white Persian cat jumped off his left sleeve! Three Siamese cats hopped off his right sleeve! A cute brown-and-white spotted kitten leaped off his collar! Soon there were cats everywhere. Ernie watched in amazement as they frolicked and played.

When the cats scampered under his bed, Ernie went after them. Quicker than he could say "Buddy Bert," he found himself in Kitten Kingdom.

Zoom! A furry car with a long tail drove by. The headlights were as bright as cats' eyes. Ernie saw a

Story by Daniel Rozenblum

Illustrations by Tom Brannon

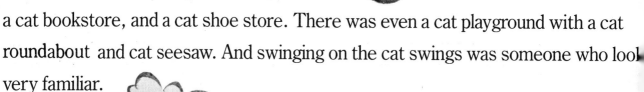

family of orange tabby cats out for an evening walk. Two striped kittens were chasing a ball of string. A black-and-white cat was sipping a bowl of milk.

Ernie's eyes grew big with wonder. He saw a cat supermarket, a cat bookstore, and a cat shoe store. There was even a cat playground with a cat roundabout and cat seesaw. And swinging on the cat swings was someone who look very familiar.

"Bert!" said Ernie. "What are *you* doing here? "Meow," answered Bert.

Ernie was so surprised that he woke up. He looked around the room. Bert was sleepin soundly. Rubber Duckie was resting on the shelf. Ernie didn't see a single cat. Then Ernie looked at his pyjamas. There they were! The fluffy, white Persian cat, the three Siamese kittens, and the black-and-white kitten sipping a bowl of milk. He saw all the other cats, too.

But where was the cute brown-and-white spotted kitty that used to be on his collar?

"Oh, well," said Ernie. "It was just a dream." And he went right back to sleep.

What do you dream about?

THINKING CORNER

Do you like cats? Why?

What do cats like to eat?

What sound does a cat make?

How many legs does a cat have?

PICNIC PLANS

Big Bird and his friends are having a picnic in the park. What foods are they sharing? Who do you think is in the picnic basket? What would you take on a picnic?

illustration by Rick Brown

STAR ⭐ SEARCH

ow many starfish can you find hidden here?

JERRY SMATH

by Jerry Smath

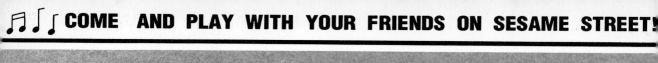
Go Up in the Clouds So High

When you look up in the clouds, do you ever imagine you can see shapes of other things? Can you touch the clouds on these two pages that look like the letters **G** and **H**? Draw a line under each letter. Can you point to the goat and the horse? Draw a circle around each cloud that looks like something whose name begins with the letter **G** or **H**

Illustration by Tom Tucker

EXTRA
Draw some cloud pictures on a piece of blue paper. Ask your friends to guess what you've drawn!

INSIDE OUT AND ALL MIXED UP

This cute little monster has gotten dressed all by himself. But look! One thing Grover has on is inside out.
Circle it.
Something else is upside down. Make an X on it. Some things are just plain silly.
Talk about each silly thing.

Illustration by Kristin Johnson

DOUBLE UP

ome of your Sesame Street friends
e inside these costumes.
ok carefully at the costumes.
hose feet do you see?
hose hair do you see?
ho is inside the horse?
hich friends are inside the giant?
old this picture up to the light
see who is inside.

Illustration by Mary Grace Eubank

Bert is **next to** Ernie.
Ernie is **next to** two of his friends.
Who is Ernie **next to**?
Grover is **on top of** Herry Monster
Who is **on top of** Grover?
Who is **between** Little Bird
and Herry Monster?
Draw a circle around the
friend who is **under** Grover.

illustration by Mary Grace Eubank

Wishful Thinking

If you had one wish, what would you wish for?
Draw your wish.

illustration © Art-so-Fine

Rubber Duckie, You're the One!

Rubber Duckie, you're the one.
You make bathtime lots of fun.
Rubber Duckie, I'm awfully fond of you.
VO-VO-DE-OH
Rubber Duckie, joys of joys.
When I squeeze you, you make noise.
Rubber Duckie, you're my very best friend, it's true.
Oh, every day when I make my way to the tubby,
I find a little fellow who's cute and yellow and chubby.
Rub-A-Dub-Dubby.
Rubber Duckie, you're so fine.
And I'm lucky that you're mine.
Rubber Duckie, I'm awfully fond of you.

Do you ever take bubble baths?
What happens when you touch a bubble?
What toys are in Ernie's bathroom?
Can all of them go in the water?
What toys do you take with you into your bathtub?

illustration by Tom